Instructions

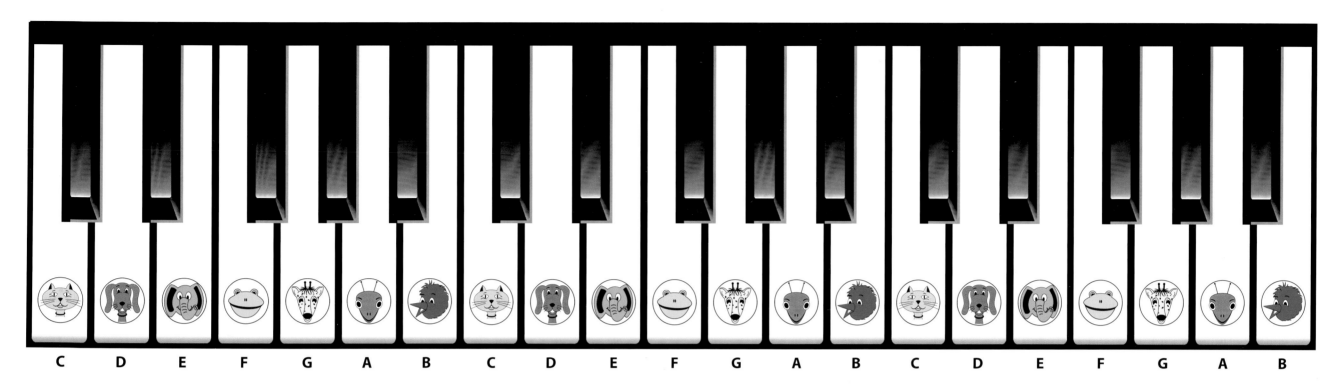

| C | D | E | F | G | A | B | C | D | E | F | G | A | B | C | D | E | F | G | A | B |

Place the stickers on the keyboard as shown above.
Write the numbers on each finger with a washable marker.

Flats ♭ and sharps ♯ no longer show this symbol
to remember the black notes.

Fingering:

Right hand finger numbers.

Left hand finger numbers.

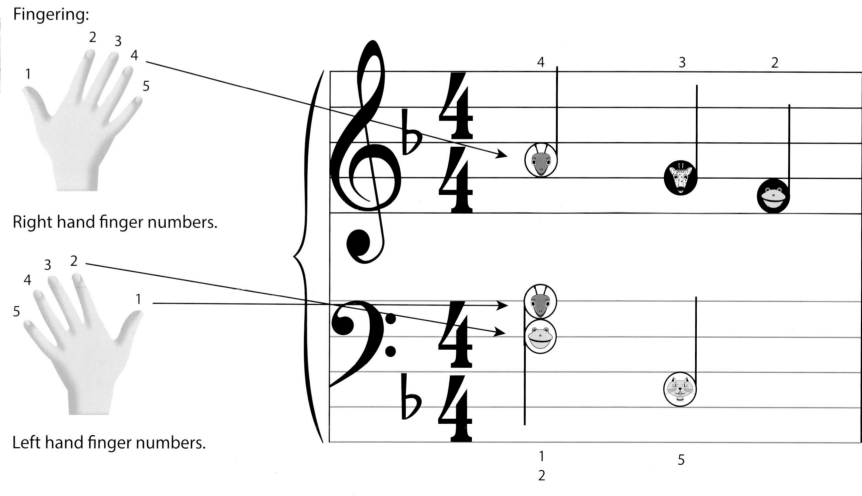

Transition to traditional music reading

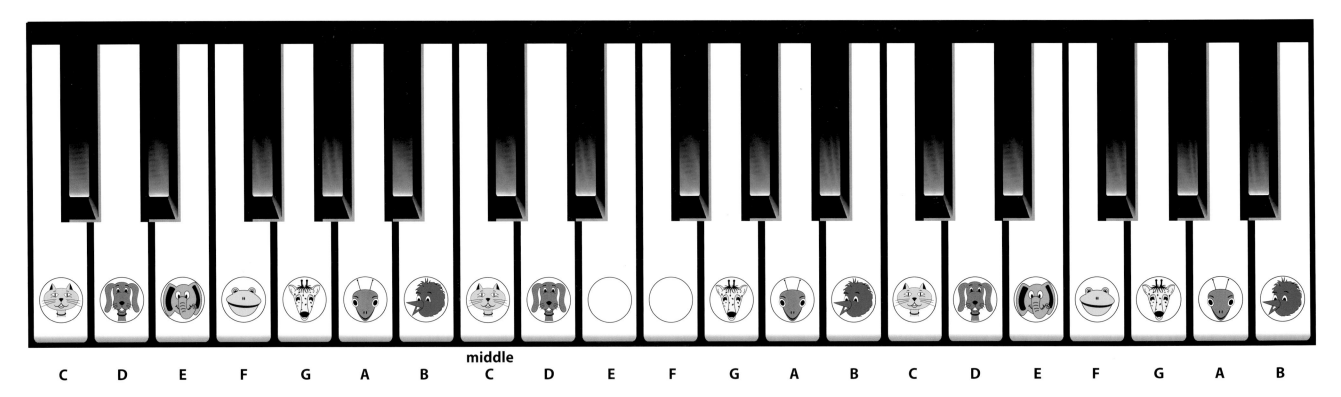

Step 1: After learning song number 1, *The Ants Go Marching*, **remove the E sticker** from the keyboard as pictured above. **Cover all E**s in the song placed in the first bottom line with a 1/4 " black or white round label. You can also use a black marker and white-out.

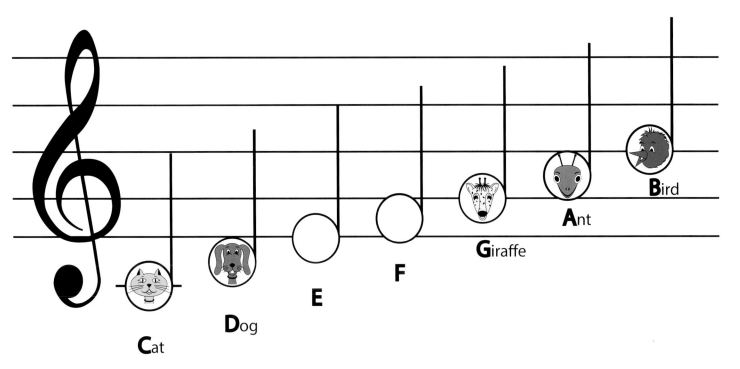

Step 2: After learning song number 3, *Little Peter Rabbit*, **remove the F sticker** from the keyboard. **Cover all F**s in the song placed on the first bottom space as described in step 1. Repeat the same steps with the adjacent stickers in the following songs.

1. The Ants Go Marching

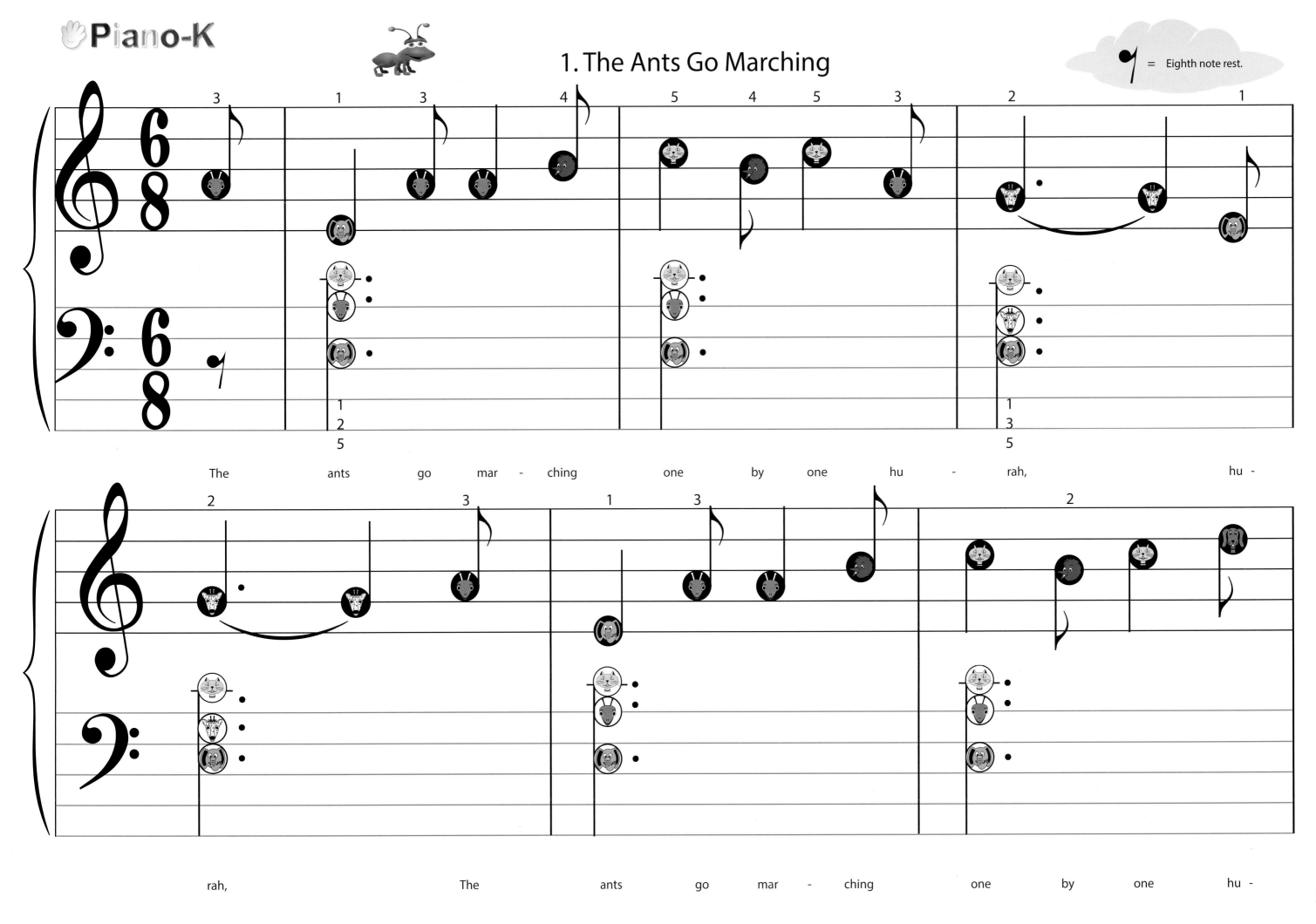

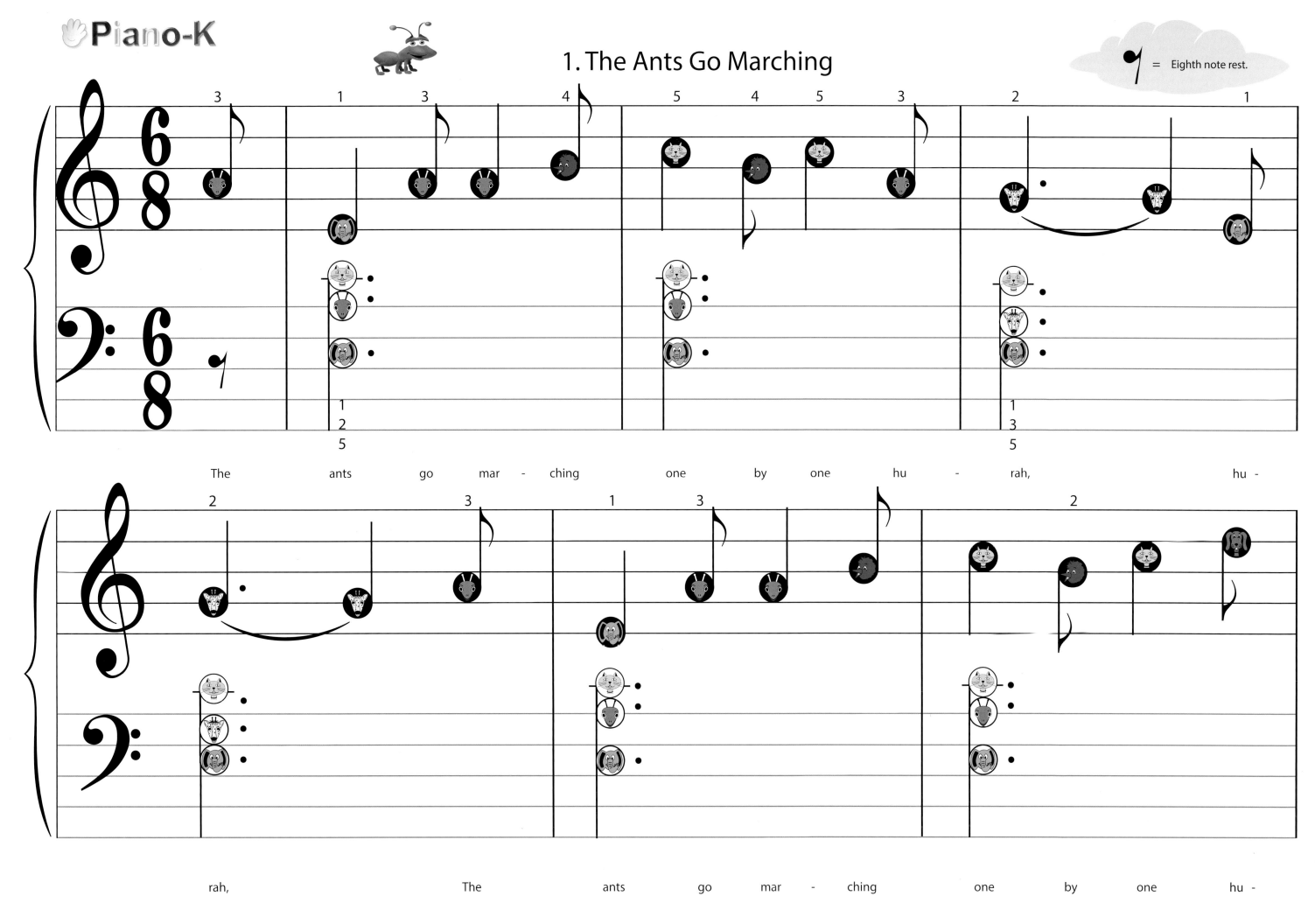

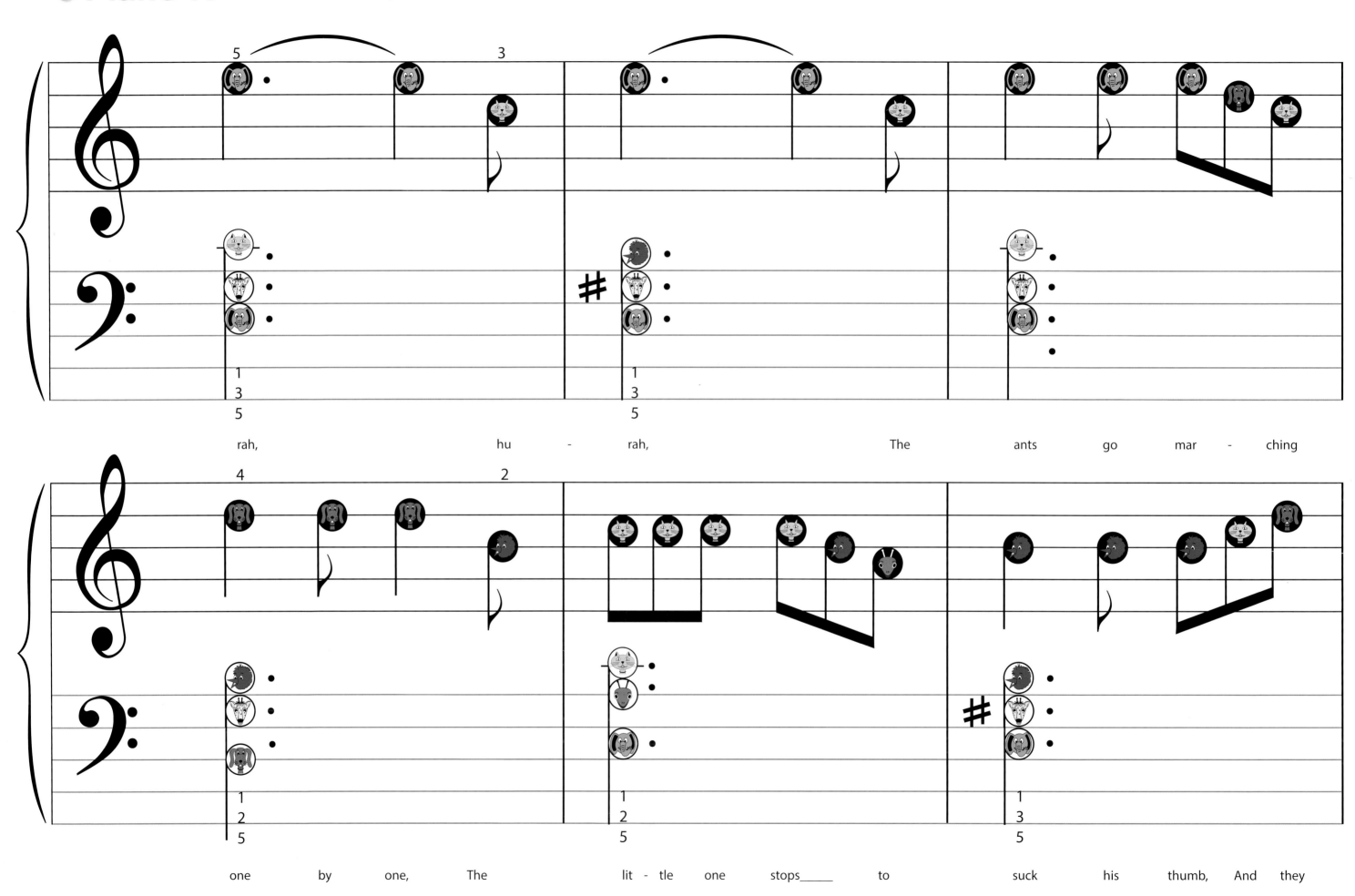

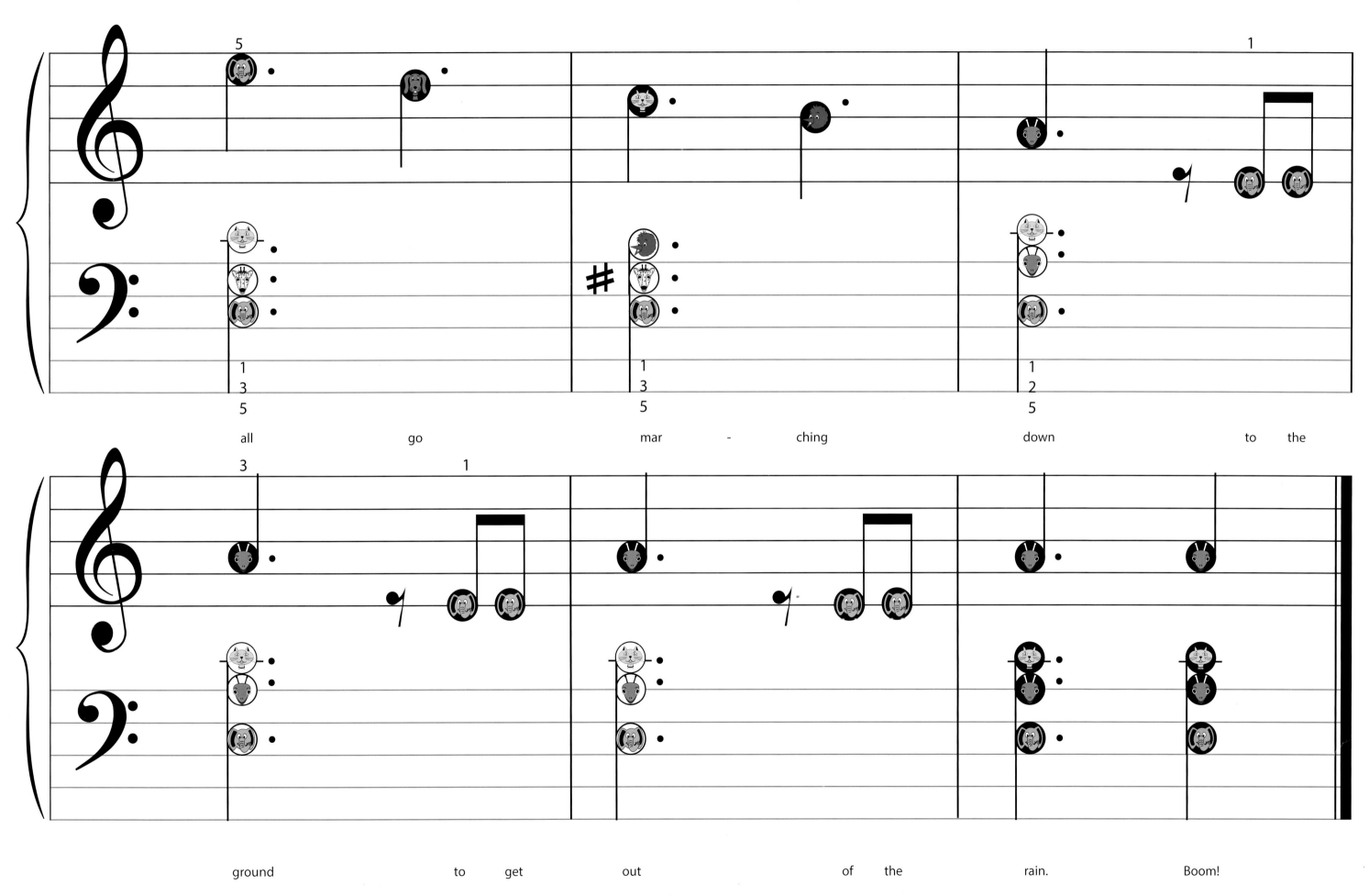

all   go   mar - ching   down   to   the

ground   to   get   out   of   the   rain.   Boom!

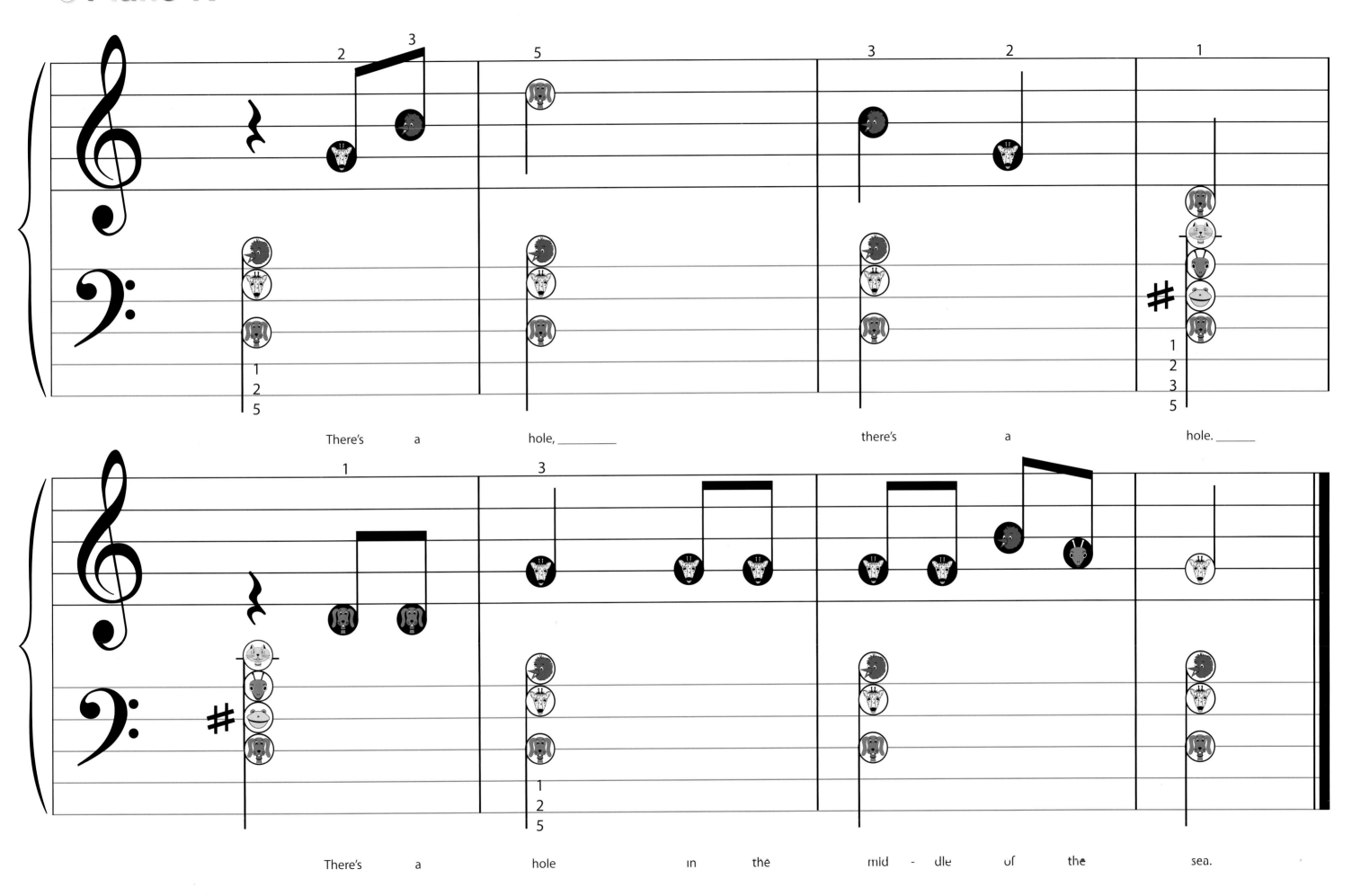

There's   a   hole, _____   there's   a   hole. _____

There's   a   hole   in   the   mid - dle   of   the   sea.

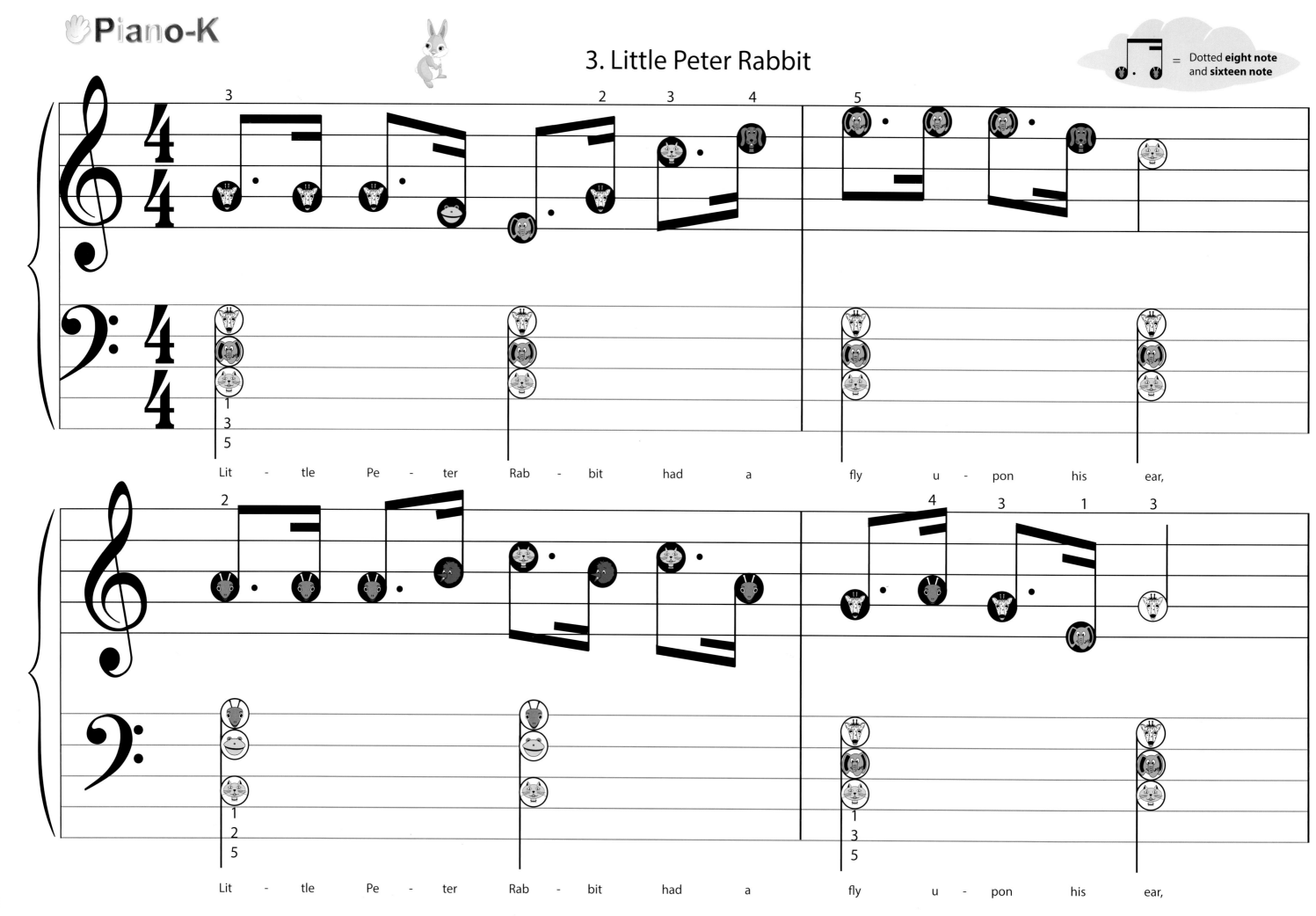

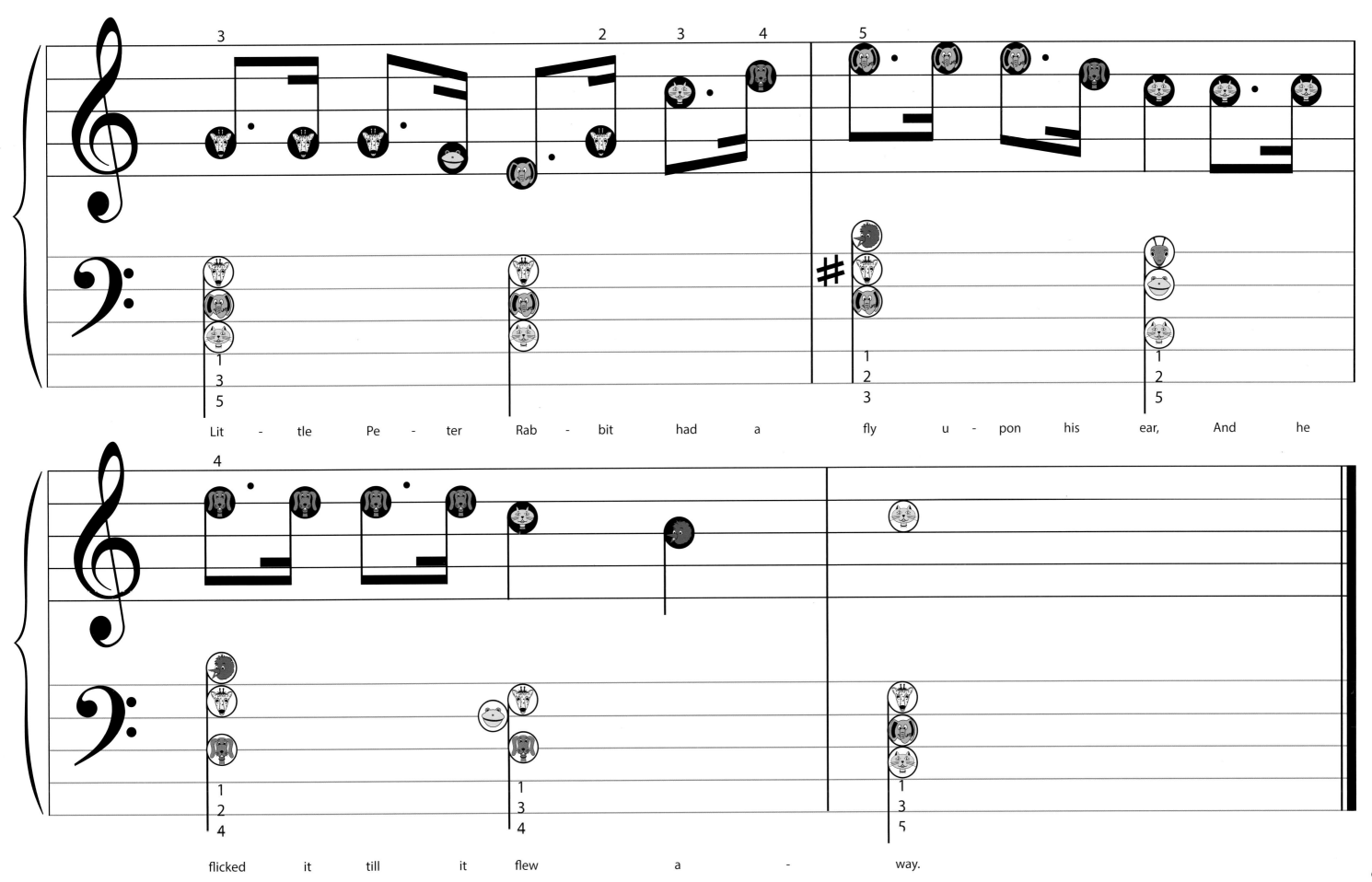

Piano-K

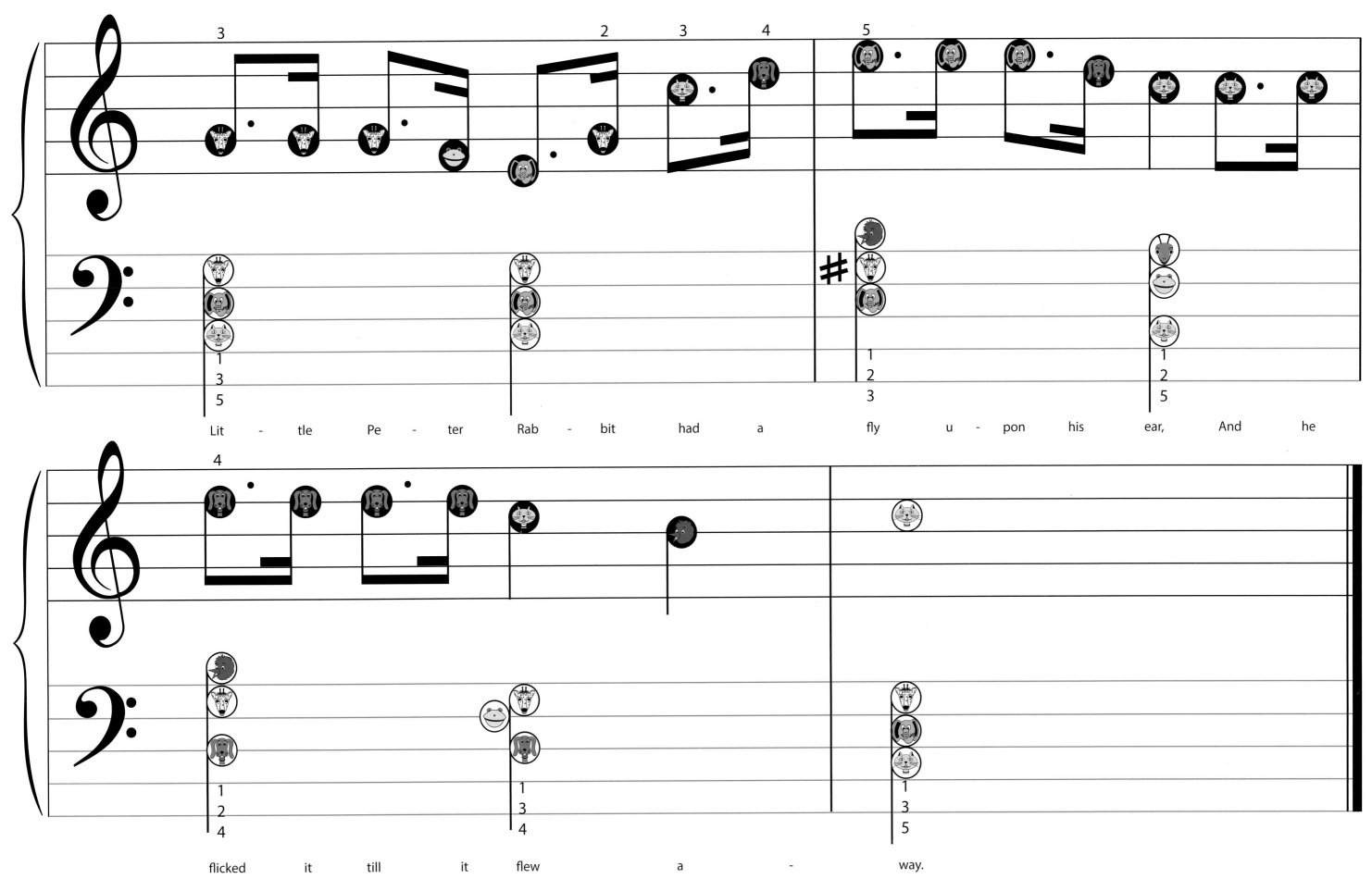

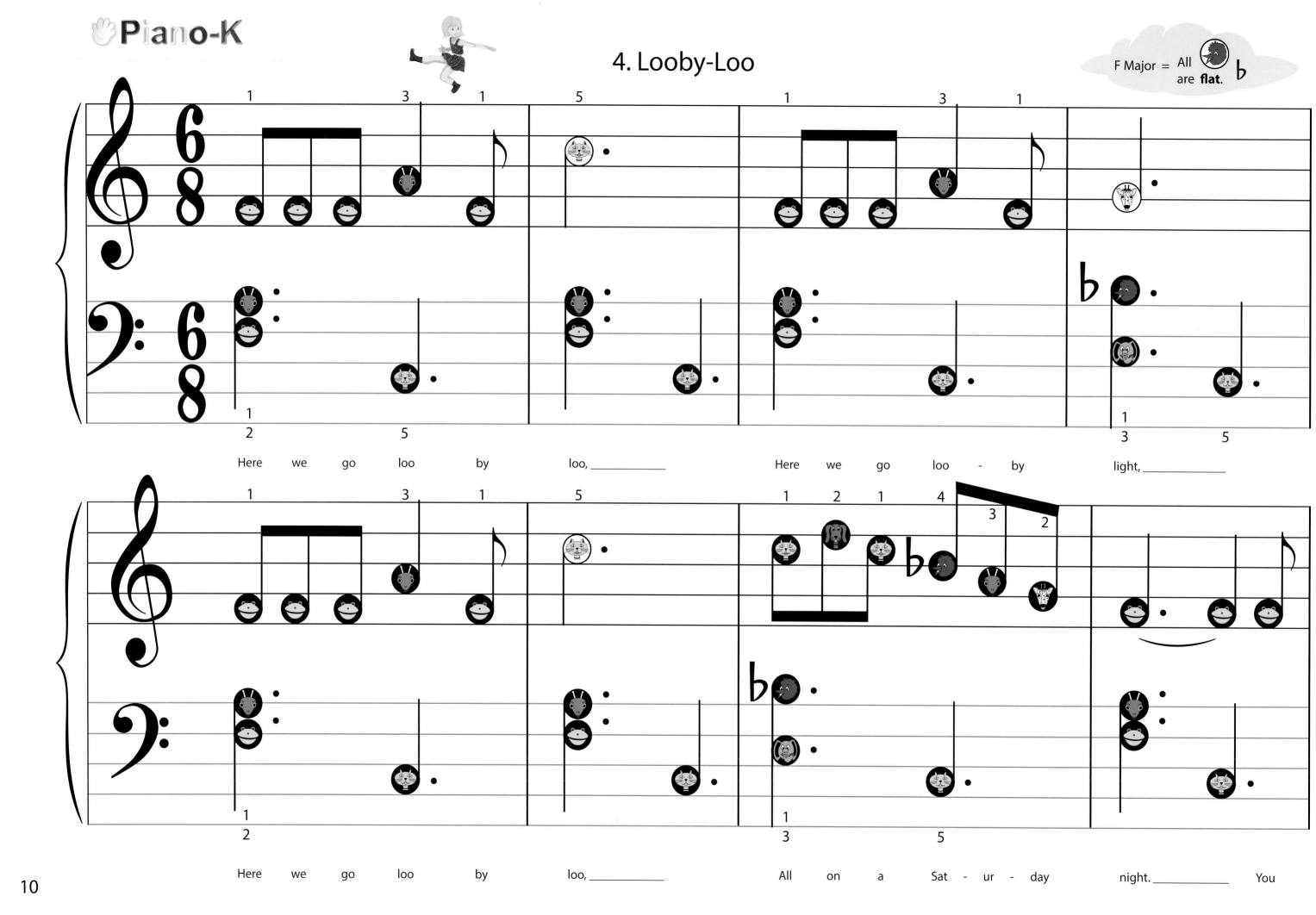

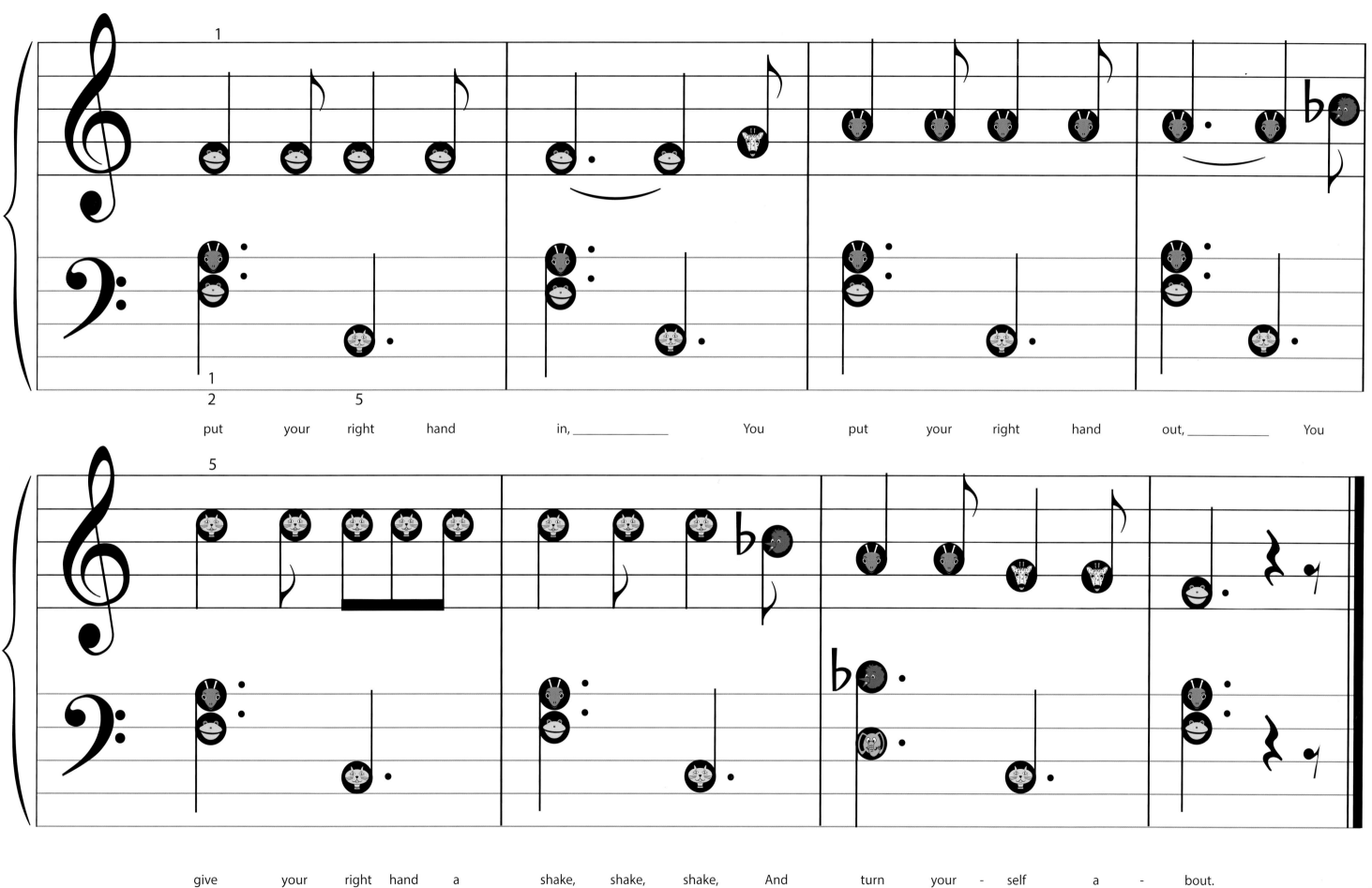

put your right hand in, _____ You put your right hand out, _____ You

give your right hand a shake, shake, shake, And turn your - self a - bout.

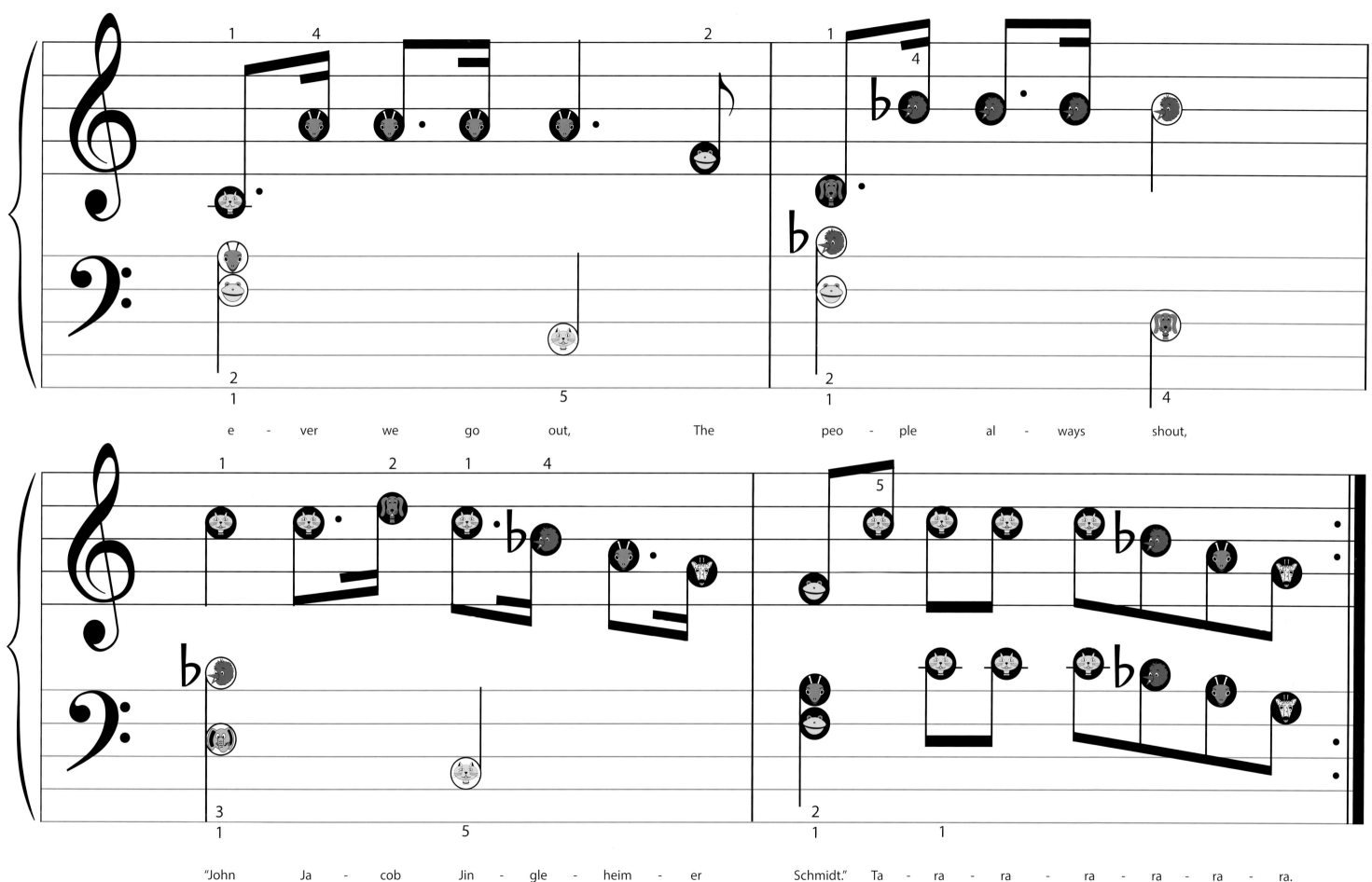

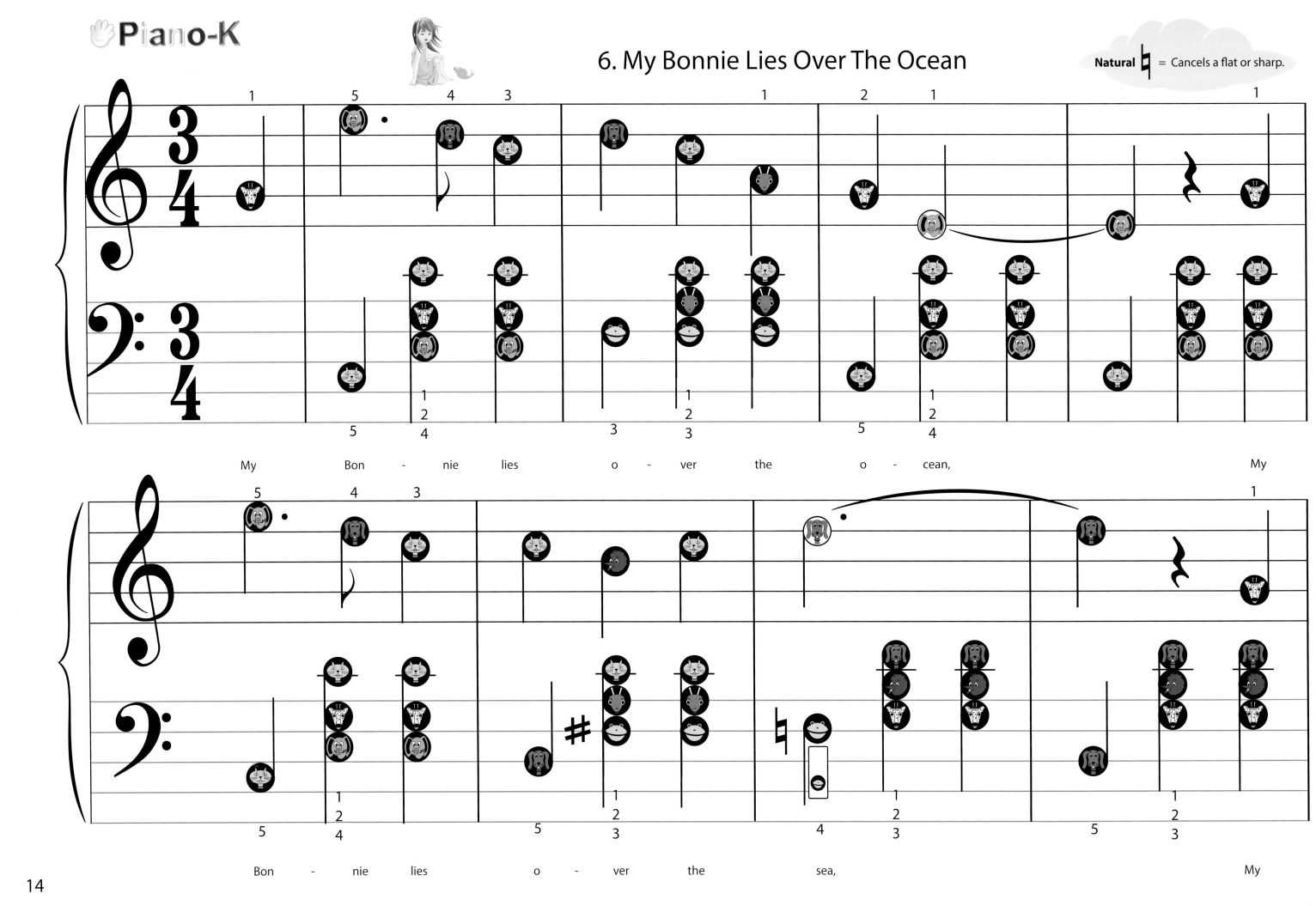

Piano-K

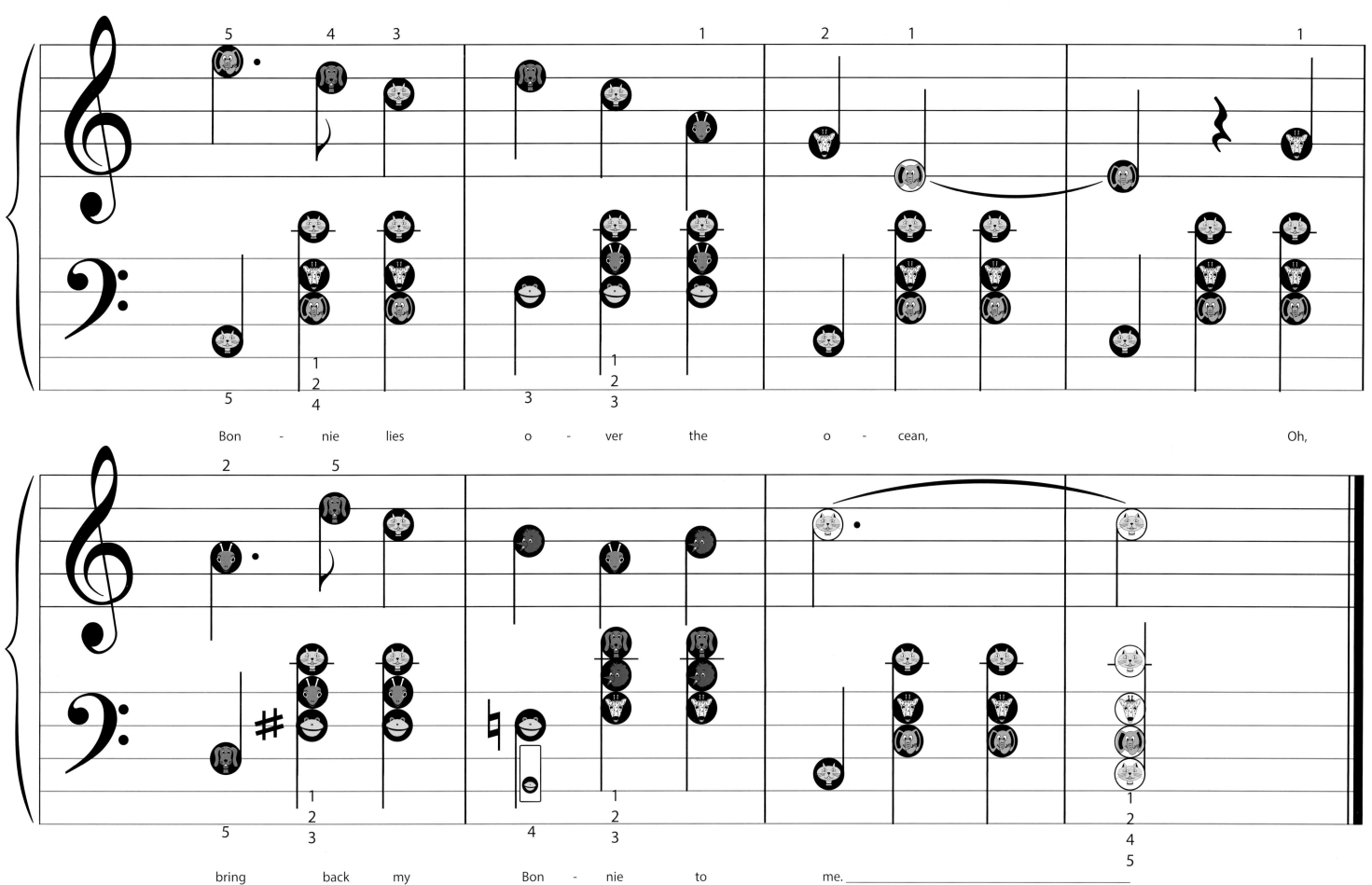

Bon - nie lies o - ver the o - cean,   Oh,

bring   back   my   Bon - nie   to   me. _____

15

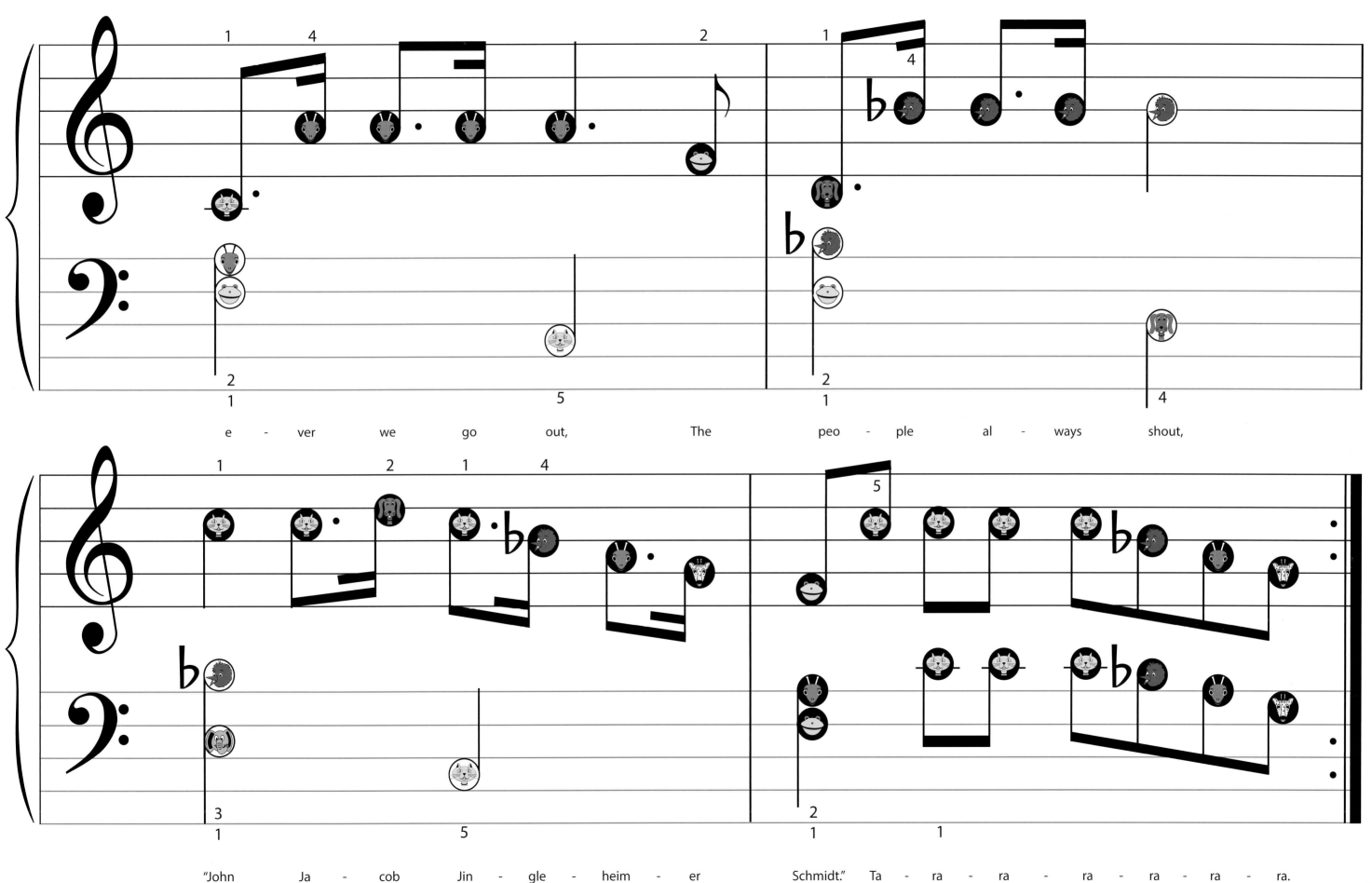

e - ver we go out, The peo - ple al - ways shout,

"John Ja - cob Jin - gle - heim - er Schmidt." Ta - ra - ra - ra - ra - ra - ra.

6. My Bonnie Lies Over The Ocean

Natural ♮ = Cancels a flat or sharp.

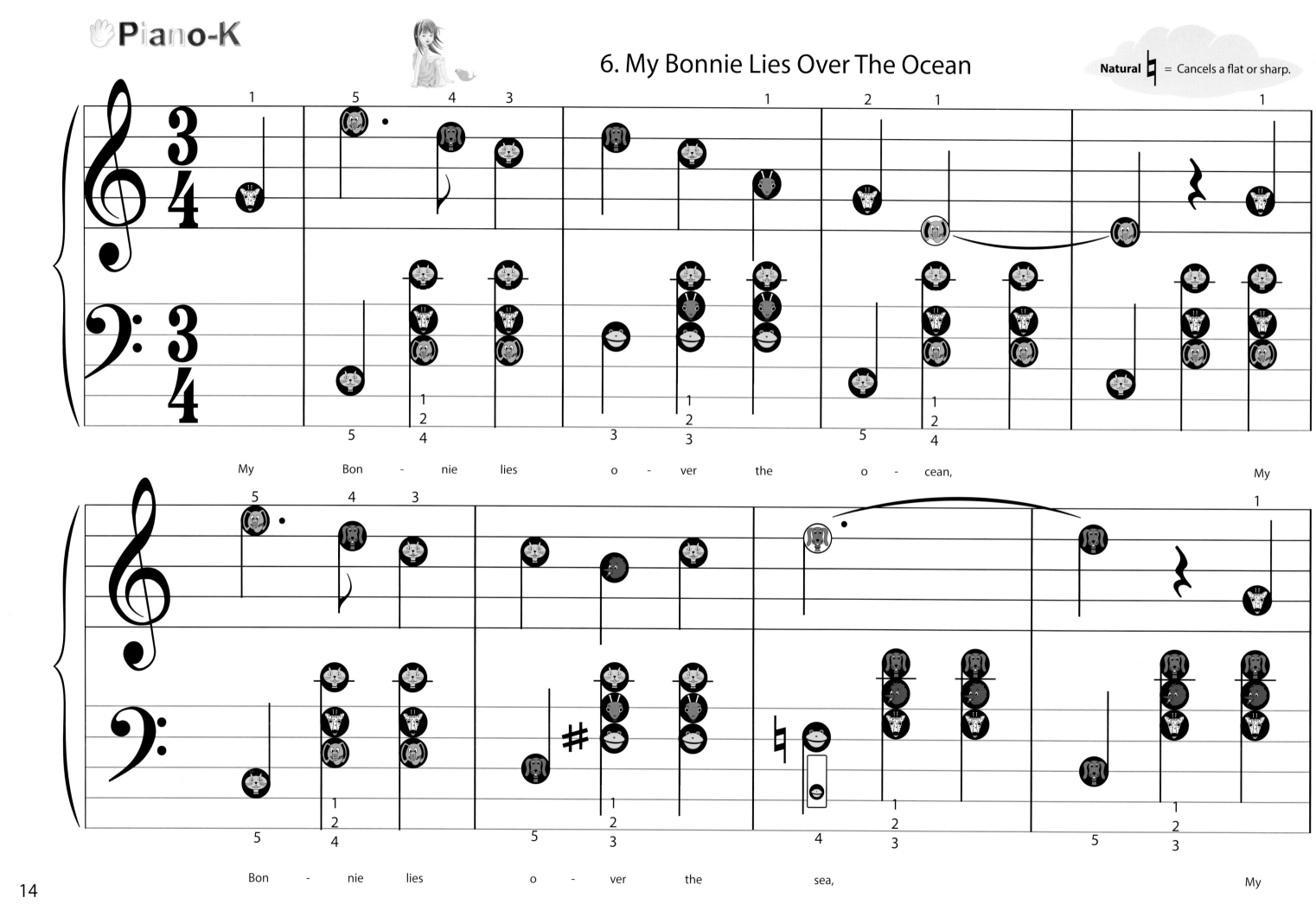

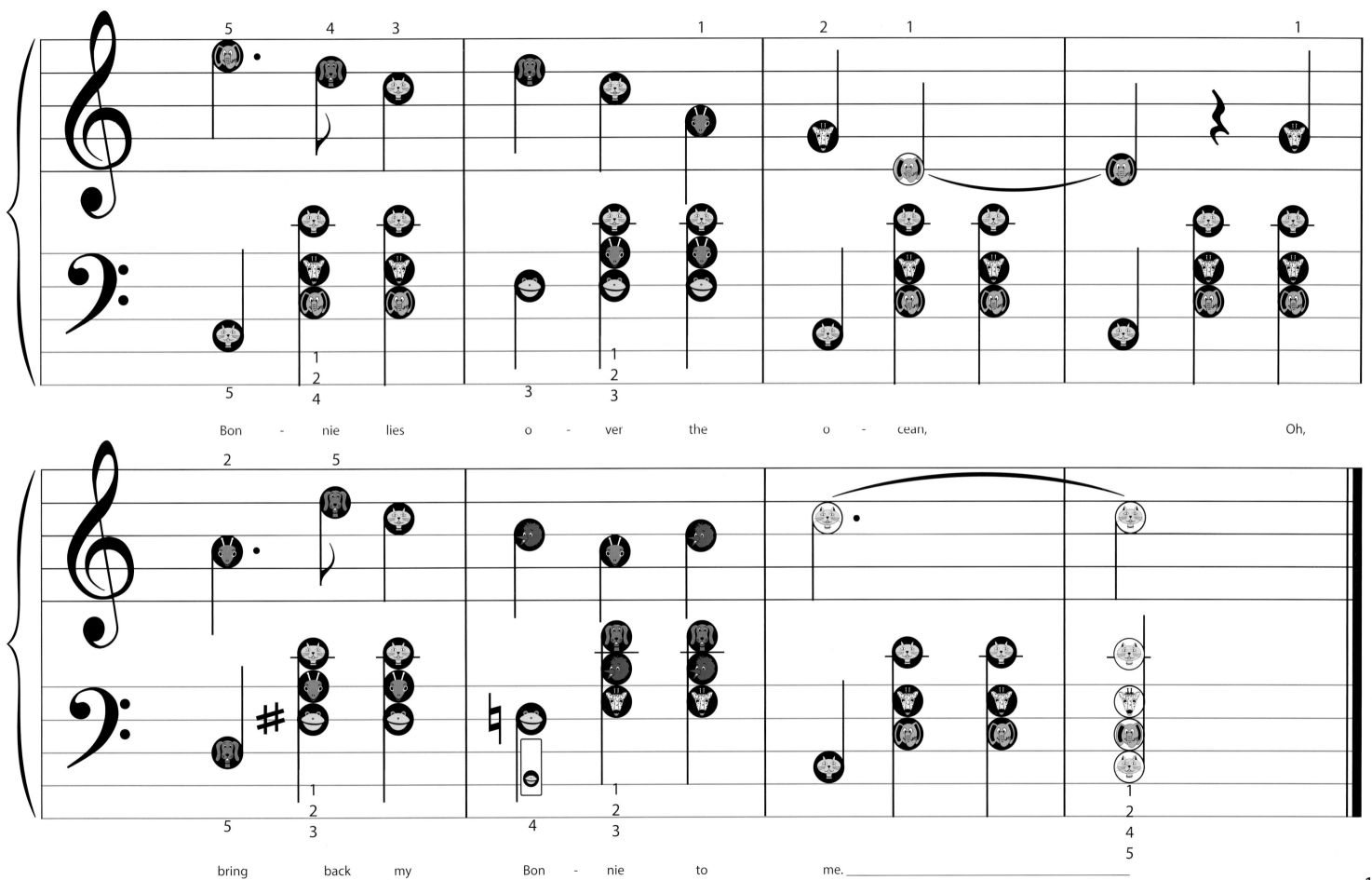

Bon - nie lies   o - ver the   o - cean,   Oh,

bring   back   my   Bon - nie   to   me. _____

15

Piano-K

8. We Wish you a Merry Christmas

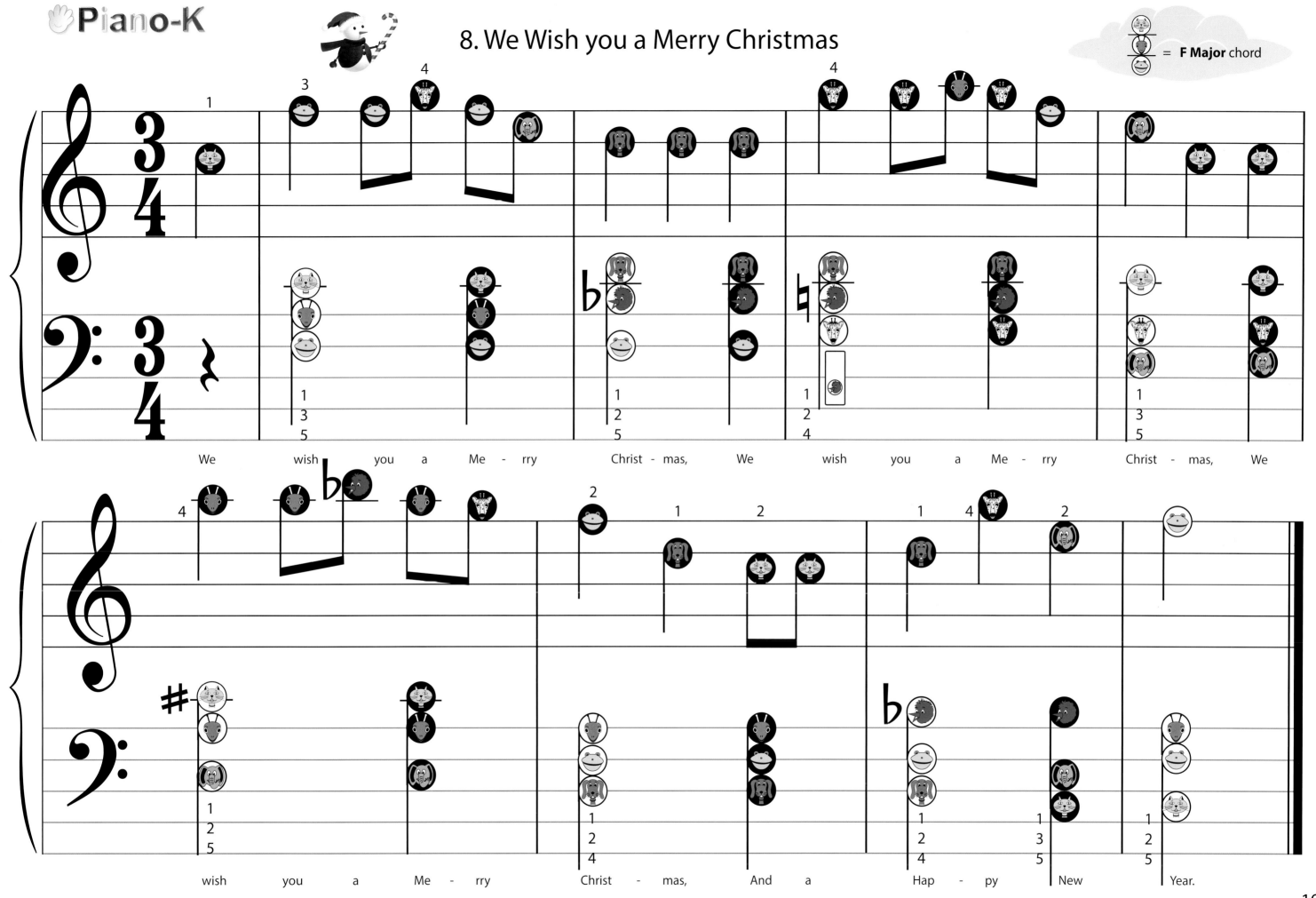

F Major chord

We wish you a Me - rry Christ - mas, We wish you a Me - rry Christ - mas, We

wish you a Me - rry Christ - mas, And a Hap - py New Year.

9. All Night, All Day

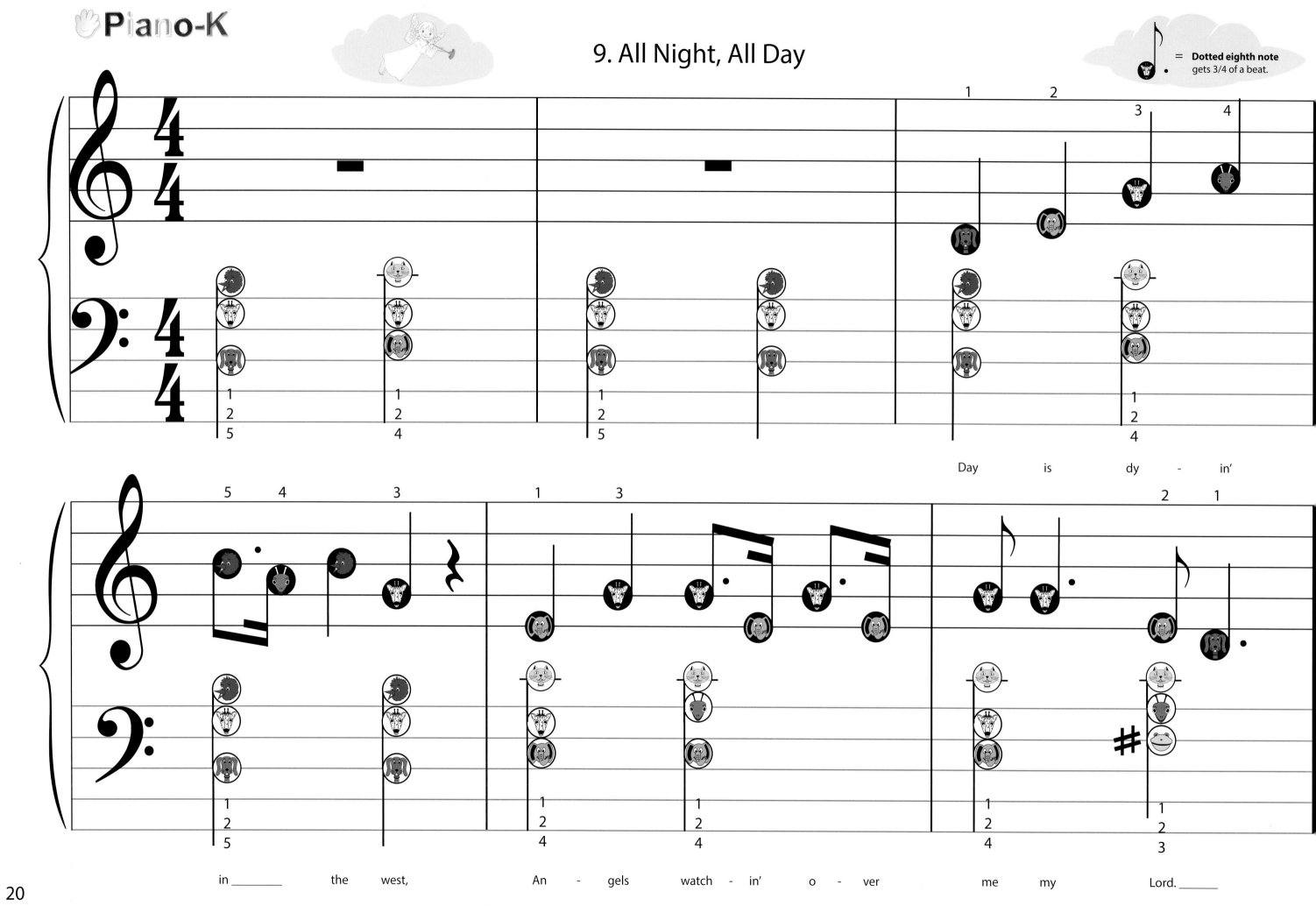

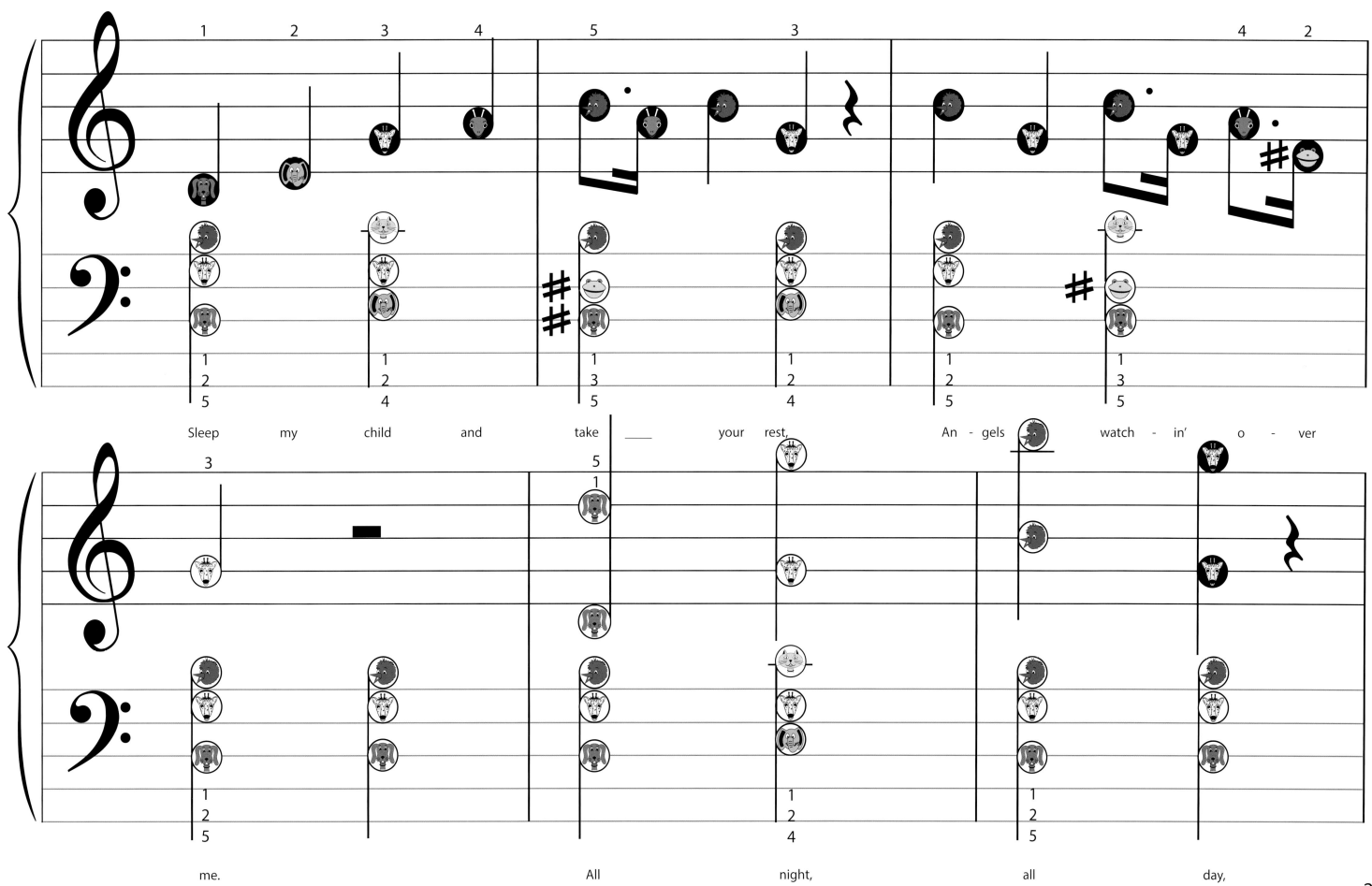

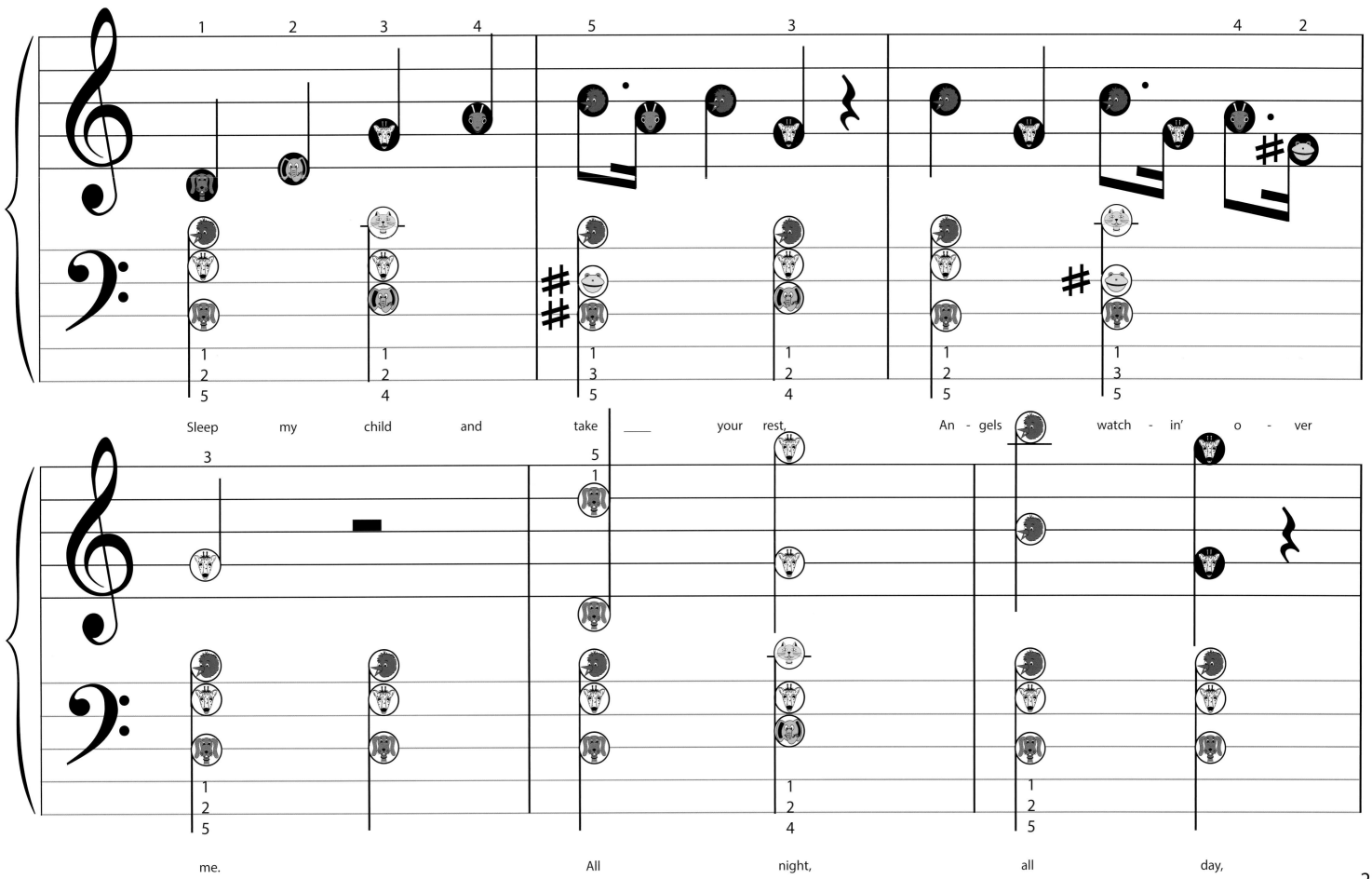

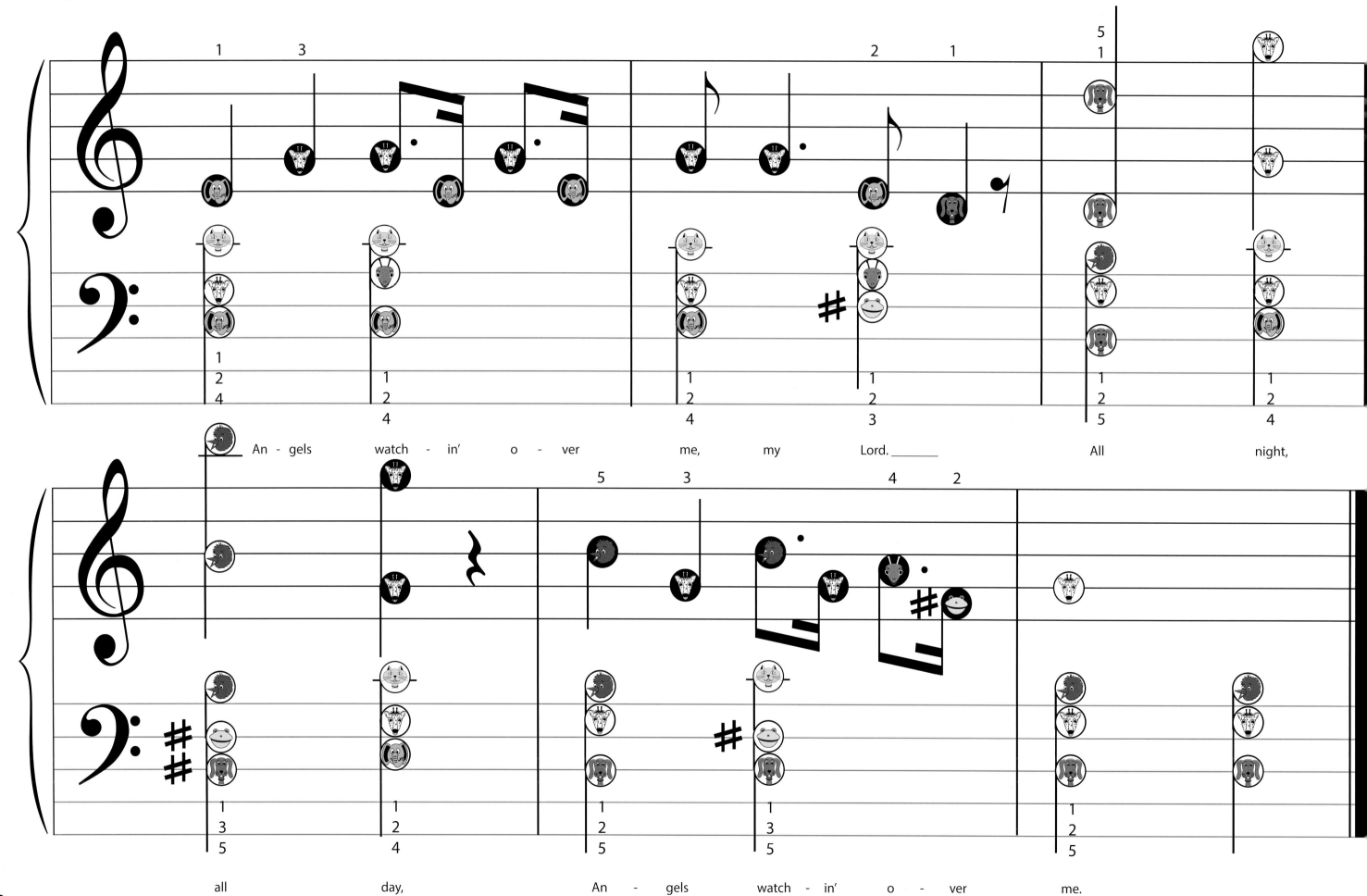

An - gels   watch - in'   o - ver   me,   my   Lord. _____   All   night,

all   day,   An - gels   watch - in'   o - ver   me.

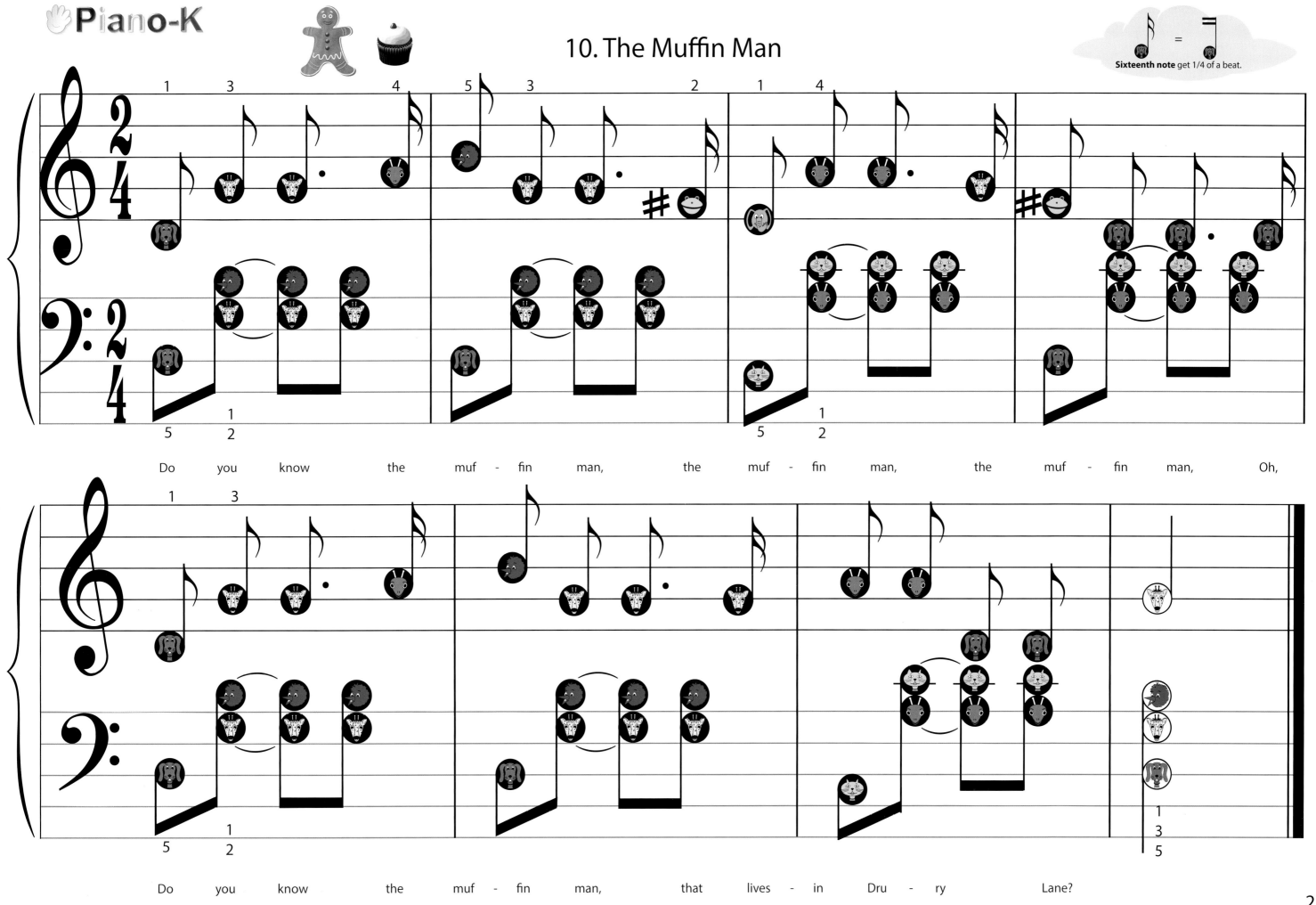

10. The Muffin Man

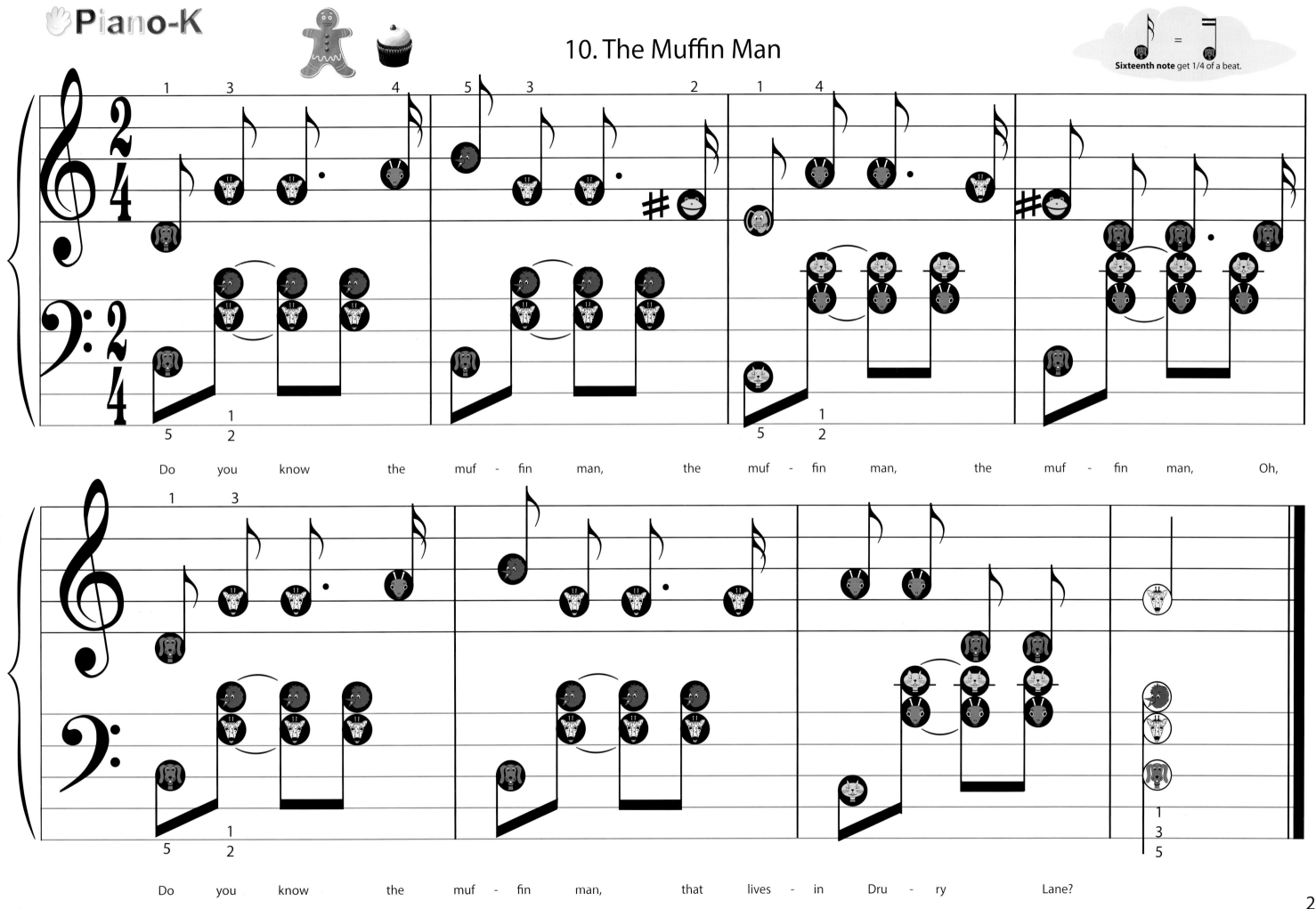

Sixteenth note get 1/4 of a beat.

Do you know the muf – fin man, the muf – fin man, the muf – fin man, Oh,

Do you know the muf – fin man, that lives – in Dru – ry Lane?

11. Minuet in G - Bach

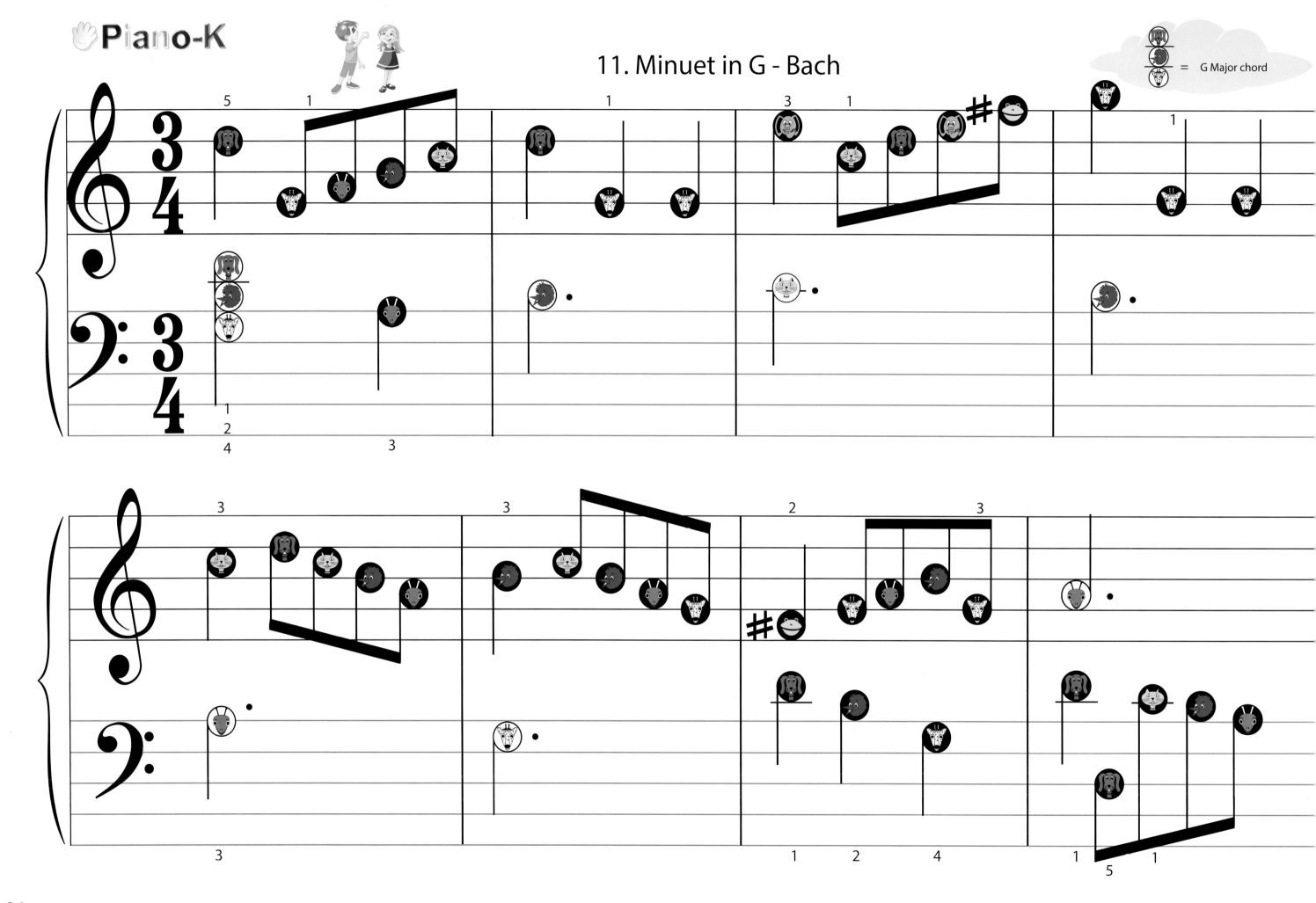

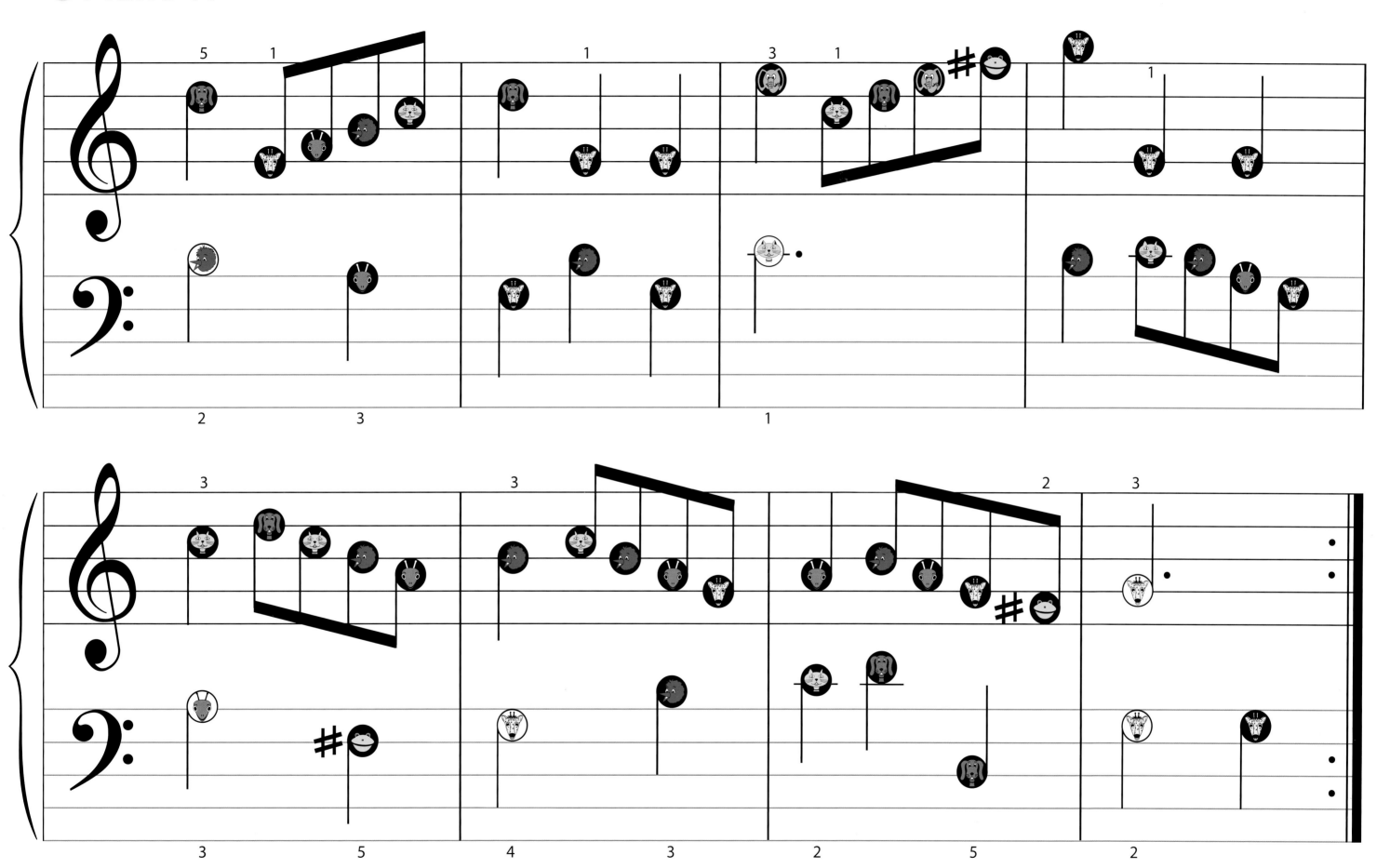

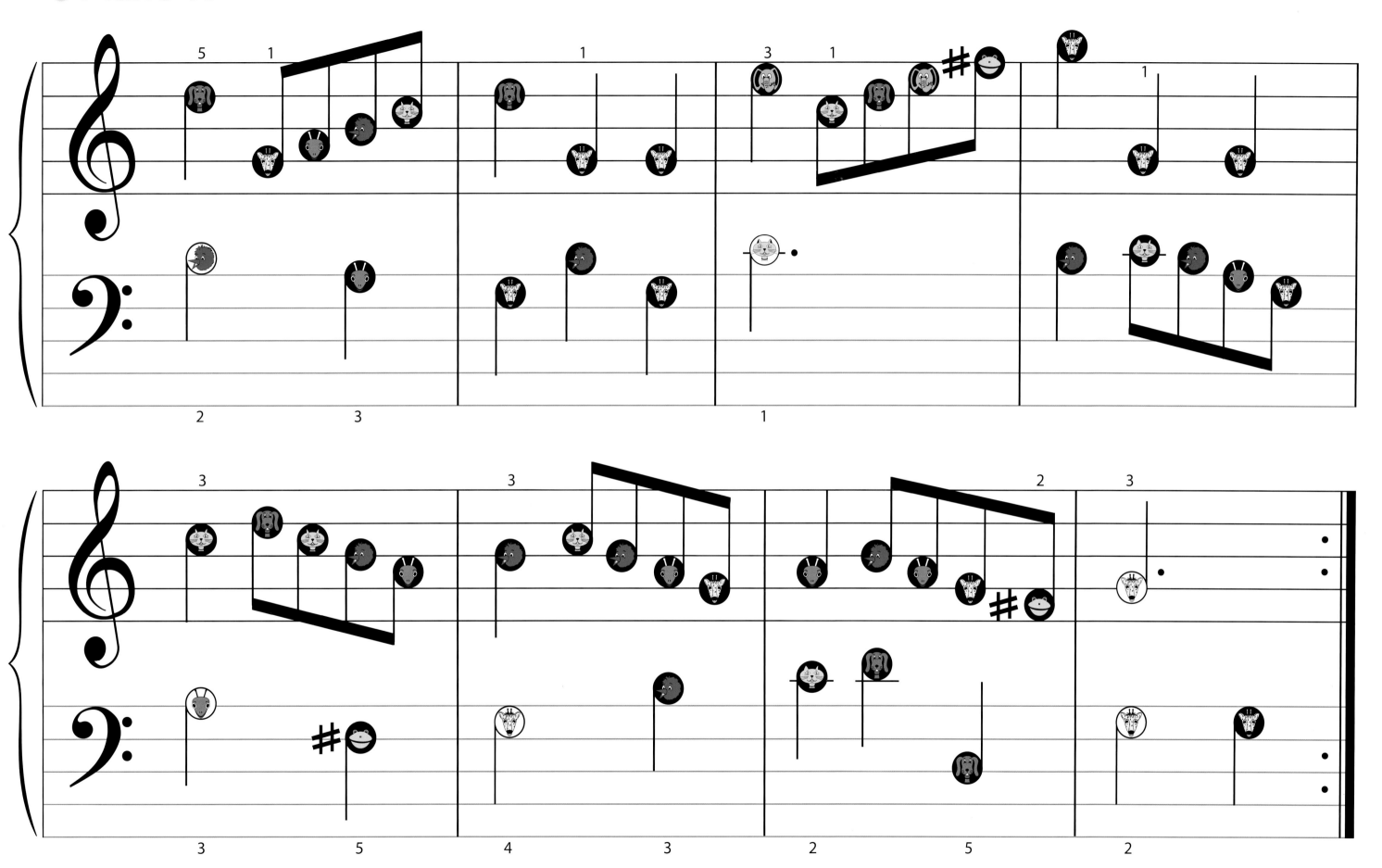

Piano-K

12. Happy Birthday

Eighth note: 1/2 beat · Dot: 1/4 beat · Sixteenth note: 1/4 beat

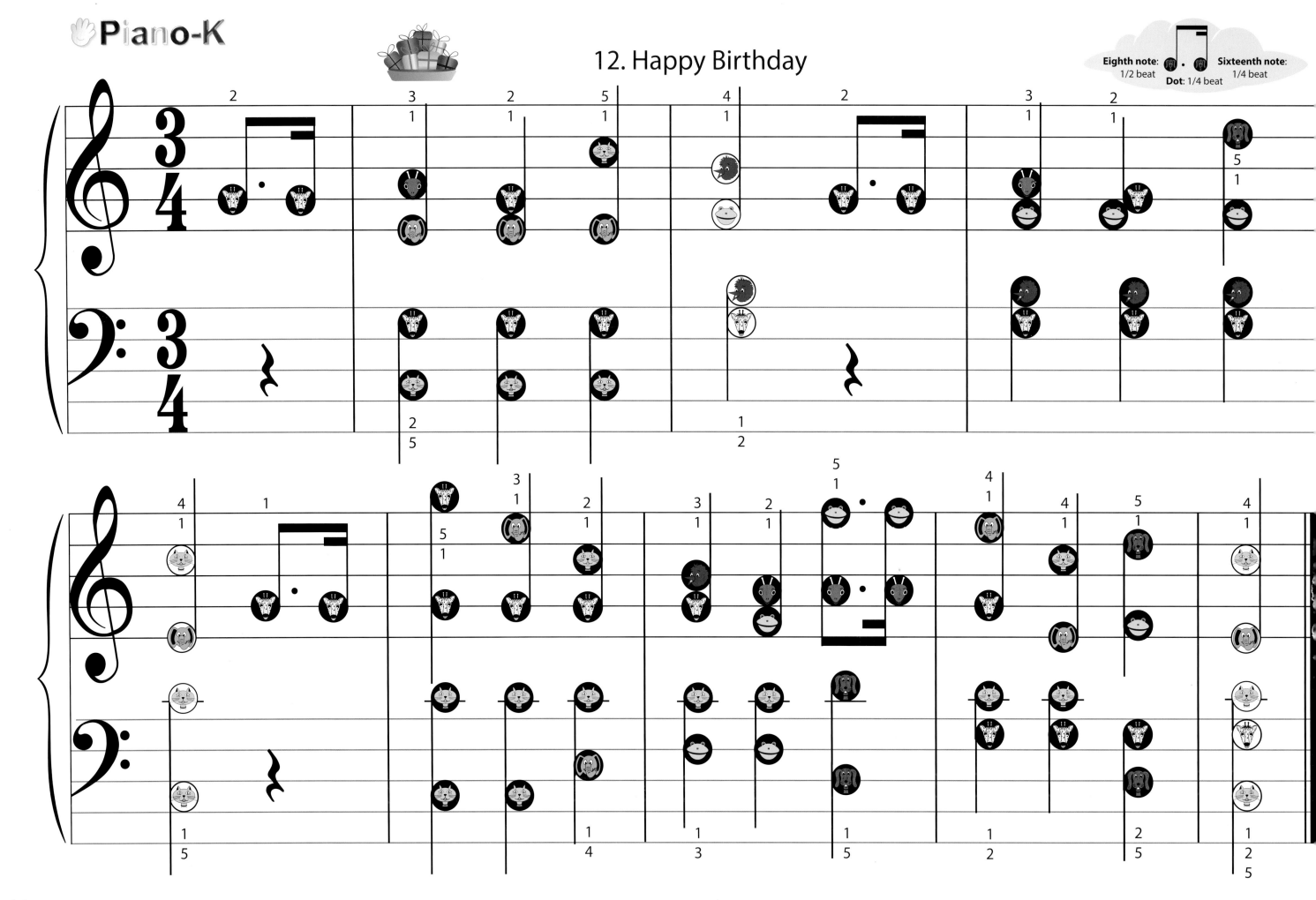